THE NORTH AMERICAN
INDIAN

PHOTOGRAPHS BY EDWARD SHERIFF CURTIS

1998 TASCHEN DIARY

The North American Indian. Edward S. Curtis

Around the turn of the century, the American photographer Edward Sheriff Curtis (1868–1952) began to work on the monumental task of recording the North American Indians, a project which was to take him more than 30 years. These photographs, his life's work, were reproduced between 1907 and 1930 in a fine-quality, massive, 20-volume publication entitled *The North American Indian*. Combining both artistic commitment and scientific interest, he managed to capture the last living traditions of the Indians in words and pictures. He demonstrated great personal dedication in visiting some 80 Indian tribes, working his way from the Mexican border to the Bering Strait. With patience and sensitivity, he succeeded in gaining the Indians' trust. By this time, they had already been herded into reservations. Their populations had been decimated to fewer than half of their original numbers, the result of wars, malnutrition and sickness, and in particular of the ongoing reduction of their living space. None of this, however, is reflected in Curtis' photographs. Instead, the images of feather-decorated Indians on horseback and the frame-filling images with expressive faces remind us more of the romantic aspects of the 19th century than of Curtis' own era, a time when the Indians were fighting for their very survival and the first automobiles were coming off the assembly line. Curtis presents the Indians as proud individuals of noble origin and so helps restore some of their erstwhile greatness. These masterly photographs conjure up a time when man and nature still seemed to be living in harmony.

A PIEGAN DANDY

SHOT IN THE HAND – APSAROKE

Los indios norteamericanos. Edward S. Curtis

El fotógrafo americano Edward Sheriff Curtis (1868–1952) inició en las postrimerías del siglo pasado y comienzos del presente su trabajo de treinta años de duración en una obra monumental sobre los indígenas norteamericanos. La obra fotográfica de toda su vida fue publicada entre 1907 y 1930 en veinte tomos con una excelente calidad de reproducción, bajo el titulo *The North American Indian*. Con un gran compromiso artístico y un profundo interés científico, Curtis captó en palabras e imágenes las huellas de la vida tradicional de los indios, que se extinguía inexorablemente. El artista visitó, bajo las condiciones más duras que puedan imaginarse, ochenta tribus indígenas, asentadas entre la frontera mexicana y el estrecho de Bering. Con paciencia y sensibilidad, Curtis logró conquistar la confianza de los indios, que ya habían sido desterrados a las reservas. Su número se había reducido drásticamente a menos de la mitad del tamaño original de sus tribus, como consecuencia de las guerras, la escasa alimentación y las enfermedades, pero muy especialmente por el incesante cercenamiento de su espacio vital. Las fotografías no reflejan ningún aspecto de esa situación. Los jinetes adornados con plumas y los expresivos rostros, que elenan toda la imagen, recuerdan mucho más el romanticismo del siglo XIX que la época de Curtis, en la que las tribus indias luchaban por asegurar su supervivencia y los primeros automóviles salían de las cadenas de montaje. Curtis muestra a los indios como seres humanos de noble origen y orgulloso porte, devolviéndoles así una parte de su primigenia grandeza. Las magistrales fotografías evocan una época en la que los seres humanos aún parecían armonizar con la naturaleza.

Les Indiens d'Amérique du Nord. Edward S. Curtis

Au tournant du siècle, le photographe américain Edward Sheriff Curtis (1868–1952) entreprend une œuvre monumentale sur les Indiens d'Amérique du Nord. Intitulée *The North American Indian*, cette œuvre d'une grande qualité photographique est publiée entre 1907 et 1930 sous forme d'une encyclopédie comportant 20 volumes. Passionné de science et de photographie, Curtis fixe par l'image et l'écrit la fin d'un monde, celui des Indiens. Il lui faudra 30 années pour mener à terme la tâche qu'il s'est fixée. Au prix de gros efforts personnels, il sillonne le pays pour visiter 80 tribus indiennes disséminées entre la frontière mexicaine et le détroit de Béring. Avec une patience infinie et une grande sensibilité, le photographe gagne la confiance des Indiens. A cette époque, ils sont déjà relégués dans des réserves. Les guerres, la sous-alimentation, les maladies et surtout la réduction continuelle de leur espace vital ont décimé la moitié de leur population totale. Les photographies de Curtis n'en laissent rien transparaître. Les cavaliers décorés de plumes et les visages expressifs, que l'on voit sur ces photos, évoquent effectivement plus le romantisme du XIXe siècle que l'époque de Curtis, où les tribus luttent pour leur survie et les premières voitures sortent des chaînes de montage. En présentant les Indiens comme des hommes de fière allure et d'origine noble, Curtis leur redonne une partie de leur grandeur passée. Ses photographies magistrales évoquent une époque où l'homme et la nature semblaient encore vivre en symbiose.

Year Planner | Plan Anual | Planning **1998**

January	Enero	Janvier		February	Febrero	Février		March	Marzo	Mars		April	Abril	Avril	
1 Th		1 Su		1 Su		1 We	
2 Fr		2 Mo	**6**	2 Mo	**10**	2 Th	
3 Sa		3 Tu		3 Tu		3 Fr	
4 Su		4 We		4 We		4 Sa	
5 Mo	**2**	5 Th		5 Th		5 Su	
6 Tu		6 Fr		6 Fr		6 Mo	**15**
7 We		7 Sa		7 Sa		7 Tu	
8 Th		8 Su		8 Su		8 We	
9 Fr		9 Mo	**7**	9 Mo	**11**	9 Th	
10 Sa		10 Tu		10 Tu		10 Fr	
11 Su		11 We		11 We		11 Sa	
12 Mo	**3**	12 Th		12 Th		12 Su	
13 Tu		13 Fr		13 Fr		13 Mo	**16**
14 We		14 Sa		14 Sa		14 Tu	
15 Th		15 Su		15 Su		15 We	
16 Fr		16 Mo	**8**	16 Mo	**12**	16 Th	
17 Sa		17 Tu		17 Tu		17 Fr	
18 Su		18 We		18 We		18 Sa	
19 Mo	**4**	19 Th		19 Th		19 Su	
20 Tu		20 Fr		20 Fr		20 Mo	**17**
21 We		21 Sa		21 Sa		21 Tu	
22 Th		22 Su		22 Su		22 We	
23 Fr		23 Mo	**9**	23 Mo	**13**	23 Th	
24 Sa		24 Tu		24 Tu		24 Fr	
25 Su		25 We		25 We		25 Sa	
26 Mo	**5**	26 Th		26 Th		26 Su	
27 Tu		27 Fr		27 Fr		27 Mo	**18**
28 We		28 Sa		28 Sa		28 Tu	
29 Th				29 Su		29 We	
30 Fr				30 Mo	**14**	30 Th	
31 Sa				31 Tu			

Year Planner | Plan Anual | Planning 1998

May | Mayo | Mai		June | Junio | Juin		July | Julio | Juillet		August | Agosto | Août	
1	Fr	1	Mo 23	1	We	1	Sa
2	Sa	2	Tu	2	Th	2	Su
3	Su	3	We	3	Fr	3	Mo 32
4	Mo 19	4	Th	4	Sa	4	Tu
5	Tu	5	Fr	5	Su	5	We
6	We	6	Sa	6	Mo 28	6	Th
7	Th	7	Su	7	Tu	7	Fr
8	Fr	8	Mo 24	8	We	8	Sa
9	Sa	9	Tu	9	Th	9	Su
10	Su	10	We	10	Fr	10	Mo 33
11	Mo 20	11	Th	11	Sa	11	Tu
12	Tu	12	Fr	12	Su	12	We
13	We	13	Sa	13	Mo 29	13	Th
14	Th	14	Su	14	Tu	14	Fr
15	Fr	15	Mo 25	15	We	15	Sa
16	Sa	16	Tu	16	Th	16	Su
17	Su	17	We	17	Fr	17	Mo 34
18	Mo 21	18	Th	18	Sa	18	Tu
19	Tu	19	Fr	19	Su	19	We
20	We	20	Sa	20	Mo 30	20	Th
21	Th	21	Su	21	Tu	21	Fr
22	Fr	22	Mo 26	22	We	22	Sa
23	Sa	23	Tu	23	Th	23	Su
24	Su	24	We	24	Fr	24	Mo 35
25	Mo 22	25	Th	25	Sa	25	Tu
26	Tu	26	Fr	26	Su	26	We
27	We	27	Sa	27	Mo 31	27	Th
28	Th	28	Su	28	Tu	28	Fr
29	Fr	29	Mo 27	29	We	29	Sa
30	Sa	30	Tu	30	Th	30	Su
31	Su			31	Fr	31	Mo 36

Year Planner | Plan Anual | Planning **1998**

September	Septiembre	Septemb		October	Octubre	Octobre		November	Noviembre	Novemb		December	Diciembre	Décemb	
1 Tu		1 Th		1 Su		1 Tu	
2 We		2 Fr		2 Mo	**45**	2 We	
3 Th		3 Sa		3 Tu		3 Th	
4 Fr		4 Su		4 We		4 Fr	
5 Sa		5 Mo	**41**	5 Th		5 Sa	
6 Su		6 Tu		6 Fr		6 Su	
7 Mo	**37**	7 We		7 Sa		7 Mo	**50**
8 Tu		8 Th		8 Su		8 Tu	
9 We		9 Fr		9 Mo	**46**	9 We	
10 Th		10 Sa		10 Tu		10 Th	
11 Fr		11 Su		11 We		11 Fr	
12 Sa		12 Mo	**42**	12 Th		12 Sa	
13 Su		13 Tu		13 Fr		13 Su	
14 Mo	**38**	14 We		14 Sa		14 Mo	**51**
15 Tu		15 Th		15 Su		15 Tu	
16 We		16 Fr		16 Mo	**47**	16 We	
17 Th		17 Sa		17 Tu		17 Th	
18 Fr		18 Su		18 We		18 Fr	
19 Sa		19 Mo	**43**	19 Th		19 Sa	
20 Su		20 Tu		20 Fr		20 Su	
21 Mo	**39**	21 We		21 Sa		21 Mo	**52**
22 Tu		22 Th		22 Su		22 Tu	
23 We		23 Fr		23 Mo	**48**	23 We	
24 Th		24 Sa		24 Tu		24 Th	
25 Fr		25 Su		25 We		25 Fr	
26 Sa		26 Mo	**44**	26 Th		26 Sa	
27 Su		27 Tu		27 Fr		27 Su	
28 Mo	**40**	28 We		28 Sa		28 Mo	**53**
29 Tu		29 Th		29 Su		29 Tu	
30 We		30 Fr		30 Mo	**49**	30 We	
		31 Sa				31 Th	

WOLF – APSAROKE

HIGH HAWK

Dec – Jan | Dic – Ene | Déc – Jan **1997/98**

Monday | Lunes | Lundi

29

Tuesday | Martes | Mardi

30

Wednesday | Miércoles | Mercredi

31

½ DAY OFF

Thursday | Jueves | Jeudi

1

New Year's Day | Jour de l'An

Friday | Viernes | Vendredi

2

Saturday | Sábado | Samedi

3

Week	2	3	4	5	6
Mo·Lu·Lu	5	12	19	26	2
Tu·Ma·Ma	6	13	20	27	3
We·Mi·Me	7	14	21	28	4
Th·Ju·Je	8	15	22	29	5
Fr·Vi·Ve	9	16	23	30	6
Sa·Sá·Sa	10	17	24	31	7
Su·Do·Di	11	18	25	1	8

4 Sunday | Domingo | Dimanche

January | Enero | Janvier **1998**

Monday | Lunes | Lundi

5

Tuesday | Martes | Mardi

6

Wednesday | Miércoles | Mercredi

7

Thursday | Jueves | Jeudi

8

Friday | Viernes | Vendredi

9

Saturday | Sábado | Samedi

10

Week	3	4	5	6	7
Mo · Lu · Lu	12	19	26	2	9
Tu · Ma · Ma	13	20	27	3	10
We · Mi · Me	14	21	28	4	11
Th · Ju · Je	15	22	29	5	12
Fr · Vi · Ve	16	23	30	6	13
Sa · Sá · Sa	17	24	31	7	14
Su · Do · Di	18	25	1	8	15

11

Sunday | Domingo | Dimanche

BIRD ON THE GROUND – APSAROKE

BEAR'S BELLY – ARIKARA

January | Enero | Janvier **1998**

Monday | Lunes | Lundi

12

Tuesday | Martes | Mardi

13

Wednesday | Miércoles | Mercredi

14

Thursday | Jueves | Jeudi

15

Friday | Viernes | Vendredi

16

Saturday | Sábado | Samedi

17

Week	4	5	6	7	8
Mo · Lu · Lu	19	26	2	9	16
Tu · Ma · Ma	20	27	3	10	17
We · Mi · Me	21	28	4	11	18
Th · Ju · Je	22	29	5	12	19
Fr · Vi · Ve	23	30	6	13	20
Sa · Sá · Sa	24	31	7	14	21
Su · Do · Di	25	1	8	15	22

18 Sunday | Domingo | Dimanche

January | Enero | Janvier **1998**

Monday | Lunes | Lundi

(USA) Martin Luther King Day

19

Tuesday | Martes | Mardi

20

Wednesday | Miércoles | Mercredi

21

Thursday | Jueves | Jeudi

22

Friday | Viernes | Vendredi

23

Saturday | Sábado | Samedi

24

Week	5	6	7	8	9
Mo · Lu · Lu	26	2	9	16	23
Tu · Ma · Ma	27	3	10	17	24
We · Mi · Me	28	4	11	18	25
Th · Ju · Je	29	5	12	19	26
Fr · Vi · Ve	30	6	13	20	27
Sa · Sá · Sa	31	7	14	21	28
Su · Do · Di	1	8	15	22	1

25 Sunday | Domingo | Dimanche

AWAITING THE RETURN OF THE SNAKE RACERS

A CHIEF'S DAUGHTER – SKOKOMISH

Monday | Lunes | Lundi

26

Tuesday | Martes | Mardi

27

Wednesday | Miércoles | Mercredi

28

Thursday | Jueves | Jeudi

29

Friday | Viernes | Vendredi

30

Saturday | Sábado | Samedi

31

Week	6	7	8	9	10
Mo · Lu · Lu	2	9	16	23	2
Tu · Ma · Ma	3	10	17	24	3
We · Mi · Me	4	11	18	25	4
Th · Ju · Je	5	12	19	26	5
Fr · Vi · Ve	6	13	20	27	6
Sa · Sá · Sa	7	14	21	28	7
Su · Do · Di	8	15	22	1	8

1

Sunday | Domingo | Dimanche

February | Febrero | Février **1998**

Monday | Lunes | Lundi

2

Tuesday | Martes | Mardi

3

Wednesday | Miércoles | Mercredi

4

Thursday | Jueves | Jeudi

5

Friday | Viernes | Vendredi

6

Saturday | Sábado | Samedi

7 *833 Parkman Dr.*
La Canada
Commonwealth Footbill

Week	7	8	9	10	11
Mo · Lu · Lu	9	16	23	2	9
Tu · Ma · Ma	10	17	24	3	10
We · Mi · Me	11	18	25	4	11
Th · Ju · Je	12	19	26	5	12
Fr · Vi · Ve	13	20	27	6	13
Sa · Sá · Sa	14	21	28	7	14
Su · Do · Di	15	22	1	8	15

8 Sunday | Domingo | Dimanche

KALISPEL TYPE

A NAKOAKTOK MÁWIHL

February | Febrero | Février **1998**

Monday | Lunes | Lundi

9

Tuesday | Martes | Mardi

Publisher's birthday. Please send
your congratulations to the following
fax number: +49 221 254919

10

Pane e Vino 10:30 651-4600

Wednesday | Miércoles | Mercredi

11

Dr. Wang 310-888-1108

Thursday | Jueves | Jeudi

12

OFF

Friday | Viernes | Vendredi

13

Saturday | Sábado | Samedi

14

Week	8	9	10	11	12
Mo·Lu·Lu	16	23	2	9	16
Tu·Ma·Ma	17	24	3	10	17
We·Mi·Me	18	25	4	11	18
Th·Ju·Je	19	26	5	12	19
Fr·Vi·Ve	20	27	6	13	20
Sa·Sá·Sa	21	28	7	14	21
Su·Do·Di	22	1	8	15	22

15

Sunday | Domingo | Dimanche

February | Febrero | Février **1998**

Monday | Lunes | Lundi

(USA) Presidents' Day

16

HOLIDAY

Tuesday | Martes | Mardi

17

Wednesday | Miércoles | Mercredi

18

10:45 AM

Dr. Norquist *626-797-2002*

Thursday | Jueves | Jeudi

19

Friday | Viernes | Vendredi

20

Saturday | Sábado | Samedi

21

Week	9	10	11	12	13
Mo · Lu · Lu	23	2	9	16	23
Tu · Ma · Ma	24	3	10	17	24
We · Mi · Me	25	4	11	18	25
Th · Ju · Je	26	5	12	19	26
Fr · Vi · Ve	27	6	13	20	27
Sa · Sá · Sa	28	7	14	21	28
Su · Do · Di	1	8	15	22	29

22 Sunday | Domingo | Dimanche

FLATHEAD MOTHER

CRATER LAKE

Feb – March | Feb – Marzo | Fév – Mars **1998**

Monday | Lunes | Lundi

23

Tuesday | Martes | Mardi

24

Wednesday | Miércoles | Mercredi

25

Thursday | Jueves | Jeudi

26

Friday | Viernes | Vendredi

27

Saturday | Sábado | Samedi

28

Week	10	11	12	13	14
Mo · Lu · Lu	2	9	16	23	30
Tu · Ma · Ma	3	10	17	24	31
We · Mi · Me	4	11	18	25	1
Th · Ju · Je	5	12	19	26	2
Fr · Vi · Ve	6	13	20	27	3
Sa · Sá · Sa	7	14	21	28	4
Su · Do · Di	8	15	22	29	5

1

Sunday | Domingo | Dimanche

March | Marzo | Mars **1998**

Monday | Lunes | Lundi **2**

Tuesday | Martes | Mardi **3**

Wednesday | Miércoles | Mercredi **4**

Thursday | Jueves | Jeudi **5**

Friday | Viernes | Vendredi **6**

Saturday | Sábado | Samedi **7**

TST-MSWID
Yamaha

818-715-0425
Starkweather

Week

Mo·Lu·Lu					
Tu·Ma·Ma					
We·Mi·M					
Th·Ju·Je					
Fr·Vi·Ve					
Sa·Sá·Sa	14	21	28	4	11
Su·Do·Di	15	22	29	5	12

SHORES OF WALKER LAKE

AT NOOTKA

March | Marzo | Mars **1998**

Monday | Lunes | Lundi

9

Tuesday | Martes | Mardi

10

Wednesday | Miércoles | Mercredi

11

Thursday | Jueves | Jeudi

12

Friday | Viernes | Vendredi

13

Saturday | Sábado | Samedi

14

Week	12	13	14	15	16
Mo · Lu · Lu	16	23	30	6	13
Tu · Ma · Ma	17	24	31	7	14
We · Mi · Me	18	25	1	8	15
Th · Ju · Je	19	26	2	9	16
Fr · Vi · Ve	20	27	3	10	17
Sa · Sá · Sa	21	28	4	11	18
Su · Do · Di	22	29	5	12	19

15

Sunday | Domingo | Dimanche

March | Marzo | Mars **1998**

Monday | Lunes | Lundi **16**

RODS 658-8832

Tuesday | Martes | Mardi **17**

Wednesday | Miércoles | Mercredi **18**

STACEY
FAT 714-220-1487

Thursday | Jueves | Jeudi **19**

Friday | Viernes | Vendredi **20**

Saturday | Sábado | Samedi **21**

Week	13	14	15	16	17
Mo·Lu·Lu	23	30	6	13	20
Tu·Ma·Ma	24	31	7	14	21
We·Mi·Me	25	1	8	15	22
Th·Ju·Je	26	2	9	16	23
Fr·Vi·Ve	27	3	10	17	24
Sa·Sá·Sa	28	4	11	18	25
Su·Do·Di	29	5	12	19	26

22 Sunday | Domingo | Dimanche

March | Marzo | Mars **1998**

Monday | Lunes | Lundi

9

Tuesday | Martes | Mardi

10

Wednesday | Miércoles | Mercredi

11

Thursday | Jueves | Jeudi

12

Friday | Viernes | Vendredi

13

Saturday | Sábado | Samedi

14

Week	12	13	14	15	16
Mo·Lu·Lu	16	23	30	6	13
Tu·Ma·Ma	17	24	31	7	14
We·Mi·Me	18	25	1	8	15
Th·Ju·Je	19	26	2	9	16
Fr·Vi·Ve	20	27	3	10	17
Sa·Sá·Sa	21	28	4	11	18
Su·Do·Di	22	29	5	12	19

15 Sunday | Domingo | Dimanche

TWO LEGGINGS – APSAROKE

MASKED DANCER – COWICHAN

March | Marzo | Mars **1998**

Monday | Lunes | Lundi

23

Tuesday | Martes | Mardi

24

Wednesday | Miércoles | Mercredi

25

Thursday | Jueves | Jeudi

26

Friday | Viernes | Vendredi

27

Saturday | Sábado | Samedi

28

Week	14	15	16	17	18
Mo · Lu · Lu	30	6	13	20	27
Tu · Ma · Ma	31	7	14	21	28
We · Mi · Me	1	8	15	22	29
Th · Ju · Je	2	9	16	23	30
Fr · Vi · Ve	3	10	17	24	1
Sa · Sá · Sa	4	11	18	25	2
Su · Do · Di	5	12	19	26	3

29 Sunday | Domingo | Dimanche

March–April | Marzo–Abril | Mars–Avril **1998**

Monday | Lunes | Lundi

30

Tuesday | Martes | Mardi

31

Wednesday | Miércoles | Mercredi

1

Thursday | Jueves | Jeudi

2

Birthday?

Friday | Viernes | Vendredi

3

Saturday | Sábado | Samedi

4

Week	15	16	17	18	19
Mo·Lu·Lu	6	13	20	27	4
Tu·Ma·Ma	7	14	21	28	5
We·Mi·Me	8	15	22	29	6
Th·Ju·Je	9	16	23	30	7
Fr·Vi·Ve	10	17	24	1	8
Sa·Sá·Sa	11	18	25	2	9
Su·Do·Di	12	19	26	3	10

5

Sunday | Domingo | Dimanche

A NAKOAKTOK CHIEF'S DAUGHTER

CAÑON DEL MUERTO – NAVAHO

April | Abril | Avril **1998**

Monday | Lunes | Lundi

6 9AM ~~Dhanono~~

50 ALESSANDRO / FAIR OAKS
SUITE (A) 30
626· 793·6141

Tuesday | Martes | Mardi

7

Wednesday | Miércoles | Mercredi

8

Thursday | Jueves | Jeudi

9

11:15
~~9:15 AM DOCTOR~~

Friday | Viernes | Vendredi

(CDN) Good Friday | Vendredi Saint

10

Saturday | Sábado | Samedi

11

Week	16	17	18	19	20
Mo·Lu·Lu	13	20	27	4	11
Tu·Ma·Ma	14	21	28	5	12
We·Mi·Me	15	22	29	6	13
Th·Ju·Je	16	23	30	7	14
Fr·Vi·Ve	17	24	1	8	15
Sa·Sá·Sa	18	25	2	9	16
Su·Do·Di	19	26	3	10	17

12 Sunday | Domingo | Dimanche

Easter Sunday | Pâques

April | Abril | Avril **1998**

Monday | Lunes | Lundi

13

Tuesday | Martes | Mardi

14

Wednesday | Miércoles | Mercredi

15

Thursday | Jueves | Jeudi

16

Friday | Viernes | Vendredi

17

Saturday | Sábado | Samedi

18

Week	17	18	19	20	21
Mo·Lu·Lu	20	27	4	11	18
Tu·Ma·Ma	21	28	5	12	19
We·Mi·Me	22	29	6	13	20
Th·Ju·Je	23	30	7	14	21
Fr·Vi·Ve	24	1	8	15	22
Sa·Sá·Sa	25	2	9	16	23
Su·Do·Di	26	3	10	17	24

19 Sunday | Domingo | Dimanche

OGLALA WAR-PARTY

THE FISHING POOL – SOUTHERN MIWOK

April | Abril | Avril **1998**

Monday | Lunes | Lundi

20

X RAY
2:30

Tuesday | Martes | Mardi

21

D2N. DUO

3290 Primavera St.
Pasadena 91107

KAT: 626-793-9123

Wednesday | Miércoles | Mercredi

22

Thursday | Jueves | Jeudi

23

Friday | Viernes | Vendredi

24

Saturday | Sábado | Samedi

25

Week	18	19	20	21	22
Mo·Lu·Lu	27	4	11	18	25
Tu·Ma·Ma	28	5	12	19	26
We·Mi·Me	29	6	13	20	27
Th·Ju·Je	30	7	14	21	28
Fr·Vi·Ve	1	8	15	22	29
Sa·Sá·Sa	2	9	16	23	30
Su·Do·Di	3	10	17	24	31

26 Sunday | Domingo | Dimanche

April – May | Abril – Mayo | Avril – Mai **1998**

Monday | Lunes | Lundi

27

Tuesday | Martes | Mardi

28

Wednesday | Miércoles | Mercredi

29

Thursday | Jueves | Jeudi

30

Friday | Viernes | Vendredi

1

Saturday | Sábado | Samedi

2

Week	19	20	21	22	23
Mo·Lu·Lu	4	11	18	25	1
Tu·Ma·Ma	5	12	19	26	2
We·Mi·Me	6	13	20	27	3
Th·Ju·Je	7	14	21	28	4
Fr·Vi·Ve	8	15	22	29	5
Sa·Sá·Sa	9	16	23	30	6
Su·Do·Di	10	17	24	31	7

3 Sunday | Domingo | Dimanche

THE EAGLE-CATCHER

ARIKARA MEDICINE CEREMONY – THE DUCKS

May | Mayo | Mai **1998**

Monday | Lunes | Lundi

11

Tuesday | Martes | Mardi

12

Wednesday | Miércoles | Mercredi

13

Thursday | Jueves | Jeudi

14

Friday | Viernes | Vendredi

15

Saturday | Sábado | Samedi

16

Week	21	22	23	24	25
Mo · Lu · Lu	18	25	1	8	15
Tu · Ma · Ma	19	26	2	9	16
We · Mi · Me	20	27	3	10	17
Th · Ju · Je	21	28	4	11	18
Fr · Vi · Ve	22	29	5	12	19
Sa · Sá · Sa	23	30	6	13	20
Su · Do · Di	24	31	7	14	21

17
Sunday | Domingo | Dimanche

May | Mayo | Mai **1998**

Monday | Lunes | Lundi

4

Tuesday | Martes | Mardi

5

Wednesday | Miércoles | Mercredi

6

Thursday | Jueves | Jeudi

7

Friday | Viernes | Vendredi

8

Saturday | Sábado | Samedi

9

Week	20	21	22	23	24
Mo · Lu · Lu	11	18	25	1	8
Tu · Ma · Ma	12	19	26	2	9
We · Mi · Me	13	20	27	3	10
Th · Ju · Je	14	21	28	4	11
Fr · Vi · Ve	15	22	29	5	12
Sa · Sá · Sa	16	23	30	6	13
Su · Do · Di	17	24	31	7	14

10 Sunday | Domingo | Dimanche

THE OATH

SPEARING SALMON

May | Mayo | Mai **1998**

Monday | Lunes | Lundi

Victoria Day | Fête de la Reine et de Dollard

Judy Lovett 7 PM

18

Tuesday | Martes | Mardi

19

Wednesday | Miércoles | Mercredi

20

Thursday | Jueves | Jeudi

21

Friday | Viernes | Vendredi

22

Saturday | Sábado | Samedi

23

Week	22	23	24	25	26
Mo·Lu·Lu	25	1	8	15	22
Tu·Ma·Ma	26	2	9	16	23
We·Mi·Me	27	3	10	17	24
Th·Ju·Je	28	4	11	18	25
Fr·Vi·Ve	29	5	12	19	26
Sa·Sá·Sa	30	6	13	20	27
Su·Do·Di	31	7	14	21	28

24

Sunday | Domingo | Dimanche

May | Mayo | Mai **1998**

Monday | Lunes | Lundi
(USA) Memorial Day

25

Tuesday | Martes | Mardi

26

Wednesday | Miércoles | Mercredi

27

Thursday | Jueves | Jeudi

28

Friday | Viernes | Vendredi

29

YELLOWSTONE

Saturday | Sábado | Samedi

30

Week	23	24	25	26	27
Mo·Lu·Lu	1	8	15	22	29
Tu·Ma·Ma	2	9	16	23	30
We·Mi·Me	3	10	17	24	1
Th·Ju·Je	4	11	18	25	2
Fr·Vi·Ve	5	12	19	26	3
Sa·Sá·Sa	6	13	20	27	4
Su·Do·Di	7	14	21	28	5

31 Sunday | Domingo | Dimanche

OVERLOOKING THE CAMP – PIEGAN

THE BOWMAN

June | Junio | Juin **1998**

Monday | Lunes | Lundi

1

Tuesday | Martes | Mardi

2

Wednesday | Miércoles | Mercredi

3

Thursday | Jueves | Jeudi

4

Friday | Viernes | Vendredi

5

Saturday | Sábado | Samedi

6

Week	24	25	26	27	28
Mo · Lu · Lu	8	15	22	29	6
Tu · Ma · Ma	9	16	23	30	7
We · Mi · Me	10	17	24	1	8
Th · Ju · Je	11	18	25	2	9
Fr · Vi · Ve	12	19	26	3	10
Sa · Sá · Sa	13	20	27	4	11
Su · Do · Di	14	21	28	5	12

7 Sunday | Domingo | Dimanche

Monday | Lunes | Lundi   **8**

Tuesday | Martes | Mardi   **9**

Wednesday | Miércoles | Mercredi   **10**

Thursday | Jueves | Jeudi   **11**

Friday | Viernes | Vendredi   **12**

Saturday | Sábado | Samedi   **13**

Week	25	26	27	28	29
Mo · Lu · Lu	15	22	29	6	13
Tu · Ma · Ma	16	23	30	7	14
We · Mi · Me	17	24	1	8	15
Th · Ju · Je	18	25	2	9	16
Fr · Vi · Ve	19	26	3	10	17
Sa · Sá · Sa	20	27	4	11	18
Su · Do · Di	21	28	5	12	19

14   Sunday | Domingo | Dimanche

BEFORE THE WHITE MAN CAME – PALM CAÑON

INVOCATION – SIOUX

June | Junio | Juin 1998

Monday | Lunes | Lundi

15

Tuesday | Martes | Mardi

16

20 Bayfrest coart
New Port Beach
92660

Wednesday | Miércoles | Mercredi

17

Thursday | Jueves | Jeudi

18

Friday | Viernes | Vendredi

19

Saturday | Sábado | Samedi

20

Week	26	27	28	29	30
Mo · Lu · Lu	22	29	6	13	20
Tu · Ma · Ma	23	30	7	14	21
We · Mi · Me	24	1	8	15	22
Th · Ju · Je	25	2	9	16	23
Fr · Vi · Ve	26	3	10	17	24
Sa · Sá · Sa	27	4	11	18	25
Su · Do · Di	28	5	12	19	26

21 Sunday | Domingo | Dimanche

June | Junio | Juin **1998**

Monday | Lunes | Lundi

22

Tuesday | Martes | Mardi

23

Wednesday | Miércoles | Mercredi

CDN Québec's National Holiday | Fête Nationale
du Québec

24

NOEL: 310 659-4334   PATIO

Thursday | Jueves | Jeudi

25

Friday | Viernes | Vendredi

26

Saturday | Sábado | Samedi

27

Week	27	28	29	30	31
Mo·Lu·Lu	29	6	13	20	27
Tu·Ma·Ma	30	7	14	21	28
We·Mi·Me	1	8	15	22	29
Th·Ju·Je	2	9	16	23	30
Fr·Vi·Ve	3	10	17	24	31
Sa·Sá·Sa	4	11	18	25	1
Su·Do·Di	5	12	19	26	2

28 Sunday | Domingo | Dimanche

THE EAGLE MEDICINE-MAN – APSAROKE

ATSINA CRAZY DANCE – THE FLIGHT OF ARROWS

June–July | Junio–Julio | Juin–Juillet **1998**

Monday | Lunes | Lundi

29

NOEL – KITCHEN FLUURS

Tuesday | Martes | Mardi

30

Wednesday | Miércoles | Mercredi

CDN Canada Day | Jour de la Confédération

1

Thursday | Jueves | Jeudi

2

Friday | Viernes | Vendredi

3

CLOSED

Saturday | Sábado | Samedi

USA Independence Day

4

Week	28	29	30	31	32
Mo·Lu·Lu	6	13	20	27	3
Tu·Ma·Ma	7	14	21	28	4
We·Mi·Me	8	15	22	29	5
Th·Ju·Je	9	16	23	30	6
Fr·Vi·Ve	10	17	24	31	7
Sá·Sá·Sa	11	18	25	1	8
Su·Do·Di	12	19	26	2	9

5 Sunday | Domingo | Dimanche

July | Julio | Juillet **1998**

Monday | Lunes | Lundi **6**

Tuesday | Martes | Mardi **7**

Wednesday | Miércoles | Mercredi **8**

Scherr
818 795-7556 |- *626-795-7556*
oct.

Thursday | Jueves | Jeudi **9**

DR. McElroy
310-264-0765 - 828-6235

Friday | Viernes | Vendredi **10**

Saturday | Sábado | Samedi **11**

Week	29	30	31	32	33
Mo·Lu·Lu	13	20	27	3	10
Tu·Ma·Ma	14	21	28	4	11
We·Mi·Me	15	22	29	5	12
Th·Ju·Je	16	23	30	6	13
Fr·Vi·Ve	17	24	31	7	14
Sa·Sá·Sa	18	25	1	8	15
Su·Do·Di	19	26	2	9	16

12 Sunday | Domingo | Dimanche

A PIEGAN PLAY TIPI

CHIEF HECTOR – ASSINIBOIN

Monday | Lunes | Lundi

13

.

Tuesday | Martes | Mardi

14

Takeshi 852-0978
OBJECTS HAIR

BATHROOM   310-652-0109   NOEL

Wednesday | Miércoles | Mercredi

15

Thursday | Jueves | Jeudi

16

11 AM HAIRCUT

Friday | Viernes | Vendredi

17

Saturday | Sábado | Samedi

18

Week	30	31	32	33	34
Mo·Lu·Lu	20	27	3	10	17
Tu·Ma·Ma	21	28	4	11	18
We·Mi·Me	22	29	5	12	19
Th·Ju·Je	23	30	6	13	20
Fr·Vi·Ve	24	31	7	14	21
Sa·Sá·Sa	25	1	8	15	22
Su·Do·Di	26	2	9	16	23

19 Sunday | Domingo | Dimanche

July | Julio | Juillet **1998**

Monday | Lunes | Lundi **20**

Tuesday | Martes | Mardi **21**

Wednesday | Miércoles | Mercredi **22**

Thursday | Jueves | Jeudi **23**

Friday | Viernes | Vendredi **24**

Saturday | Sábado | Samedi **25**

Week	31	32	33	34	35
Mo·Lu·Lu	27	3	10	17	24
Tu·Ma·Ma	28	4	11	18	25
We·Mi·Me	29	5	12	19	26
Th·Ju·Je	30	6	13	20	27
Fr·Vi·Ve	31	7	14	21	28
Sa·Sá·Sa	1	8	15	22	29
Su·Do·Di	2	9	16	23	30

26 Sunday | Domingo | Dimanche

AT THE WATER'S EDGE – PIEGAN

FISHING CAMP – LAKE POMO

July – Aug | Julio – Ago | Juillet – Août **1998**

Monday | Lunes | Lundi **27**

Tuesday | Martes | Mardi **28**

Dr Wang 310-888-1108

Wednesday | Miércoles | Mercredi **29**

Thursday | Jueves | Jeudi **30**

KEFLEX
FOSAMAX
EVISTA   *397 3737*

Friday | Viernes | Vendredi **31**

Saturday | Sábado | Samedi **1**

Week	32	33	34	35	36
Mo·Lu·Lu	3	10	17	24	31
Tu·Ma·Ma	4	11	18	25	1
We·Mi·Me	5	12	19	26	2
Th·Ju·Je	6	13	20	27	3
Fr·Vi·Ve	7	14	21	28	4
Sa·Sá·Sa	8	15	22	29	5
Su·Do·Di	9	16	23	30	6

2 Sunday | Domingo | Dimanche

August | Agosto | Août **1998**

Monday | Lunes | Lundi

3

sick

Tuesday | Martes | Mardi

4

Wednesday | Miércoles | Mercredi

5

Thursday | Jueves | Jeudi

6

Friday | Viernes | Vendredi

7

Saturday | Sábado | Samedi

8

Week	33	34	35	36	37
Mo · Lu · Lu	10	17	24	31	7
Tu · Ma · Ma	11	18	25	1	8
We · Mi · Me	12	19	26	2	9
Th · Ju · Je	13	20	27	3	10
Fr · Vi · Ve	14	21	28	4	11
Sa · Sá · Sa	15	22	29	5	12
Su · Do · Di	16	23	30	6	13

9 Sunday | Domingo | Dimanche

Vent Fair To 16th

THE RUSH GATHERER – KUTENAI

A SMOKY DAY AT THE SUGAR BOWL – HUPA

August | Agosto | Août **1998**

Monday | Lunes | Lundi

10

Tuesday | Martes | Mardi

11

Wednesday | Miércoles | Mercredi

12

Thursday | Jueves | Jeudi

13

KOONTZ - 310-652-0123

Friday | Viernes | Vendredi

14

Monterey

Saturday | Sábado | Samedi

15

Week	34	35	36	37	38
Mo·Lu·Lu	17	24	31	7	14
Tu·Ma·Ma	18	25	1	8	15
We·Mi·Me	19	26	2	9	16
Th·Ju·Je	20	27	3	10	17
Fr·Vi·Ve	21	28	4	11	18
Sa·Sá·Sa	22	29	5	12	19
Su·Do·Di	23	30	6	13	20

16 Sunday | Domingo | Dimanche

August | Agosto | Août **1998**

Monday | Lunes | Lundi **17**

Dr Smidt
310 old 310 - 264-0065
828-6235 310-828-6235

Tuesday | Martes | Mardi **18**

Wednesday | Miércoles | Mercredi **19**

TAKESHi NOON

Thursday | Jueves | Jeudi **20**

Friday | Viernes | Vendredi **21**

OFF

Saturday | Sábado | Samedi **22**

Week	35	36	37	38	39
Mo·Lu·Lu	24	31	7	14	21
Tu·Ma·Ma	25	1	8	15	22
We·Mi·Me	26	2	9	16	23
Th·Ju·Je	27	3	10	17	24
Fr·Vi·Ve	28	4	11	18	25
Sa·Sá·Sa	29	5	12	19	26
Su·Do·Di	30	6	13	20	27

23 Sunday | Domingo | Dimanche

ON THE SHORES AT NOOTKA

THE PRIMITIVE ARTIST – PAVIOTSO

August | Agosto | Août **1998**

Monday | Lunes | Lundi

24

Tuesday | Martes | Mardi

25

Wednesday | Miércoles | Mercredi

26

Thursday | Jueves | Jeudi

27

Ko Thursday 7:30

Friday | Viernes | Vendredi

28

Saturday | Sábado | Samedi

29

Week	36	37	38	39	40
Mo · Lu · Lu	31	7	14	21	28
Tu · Ma · Ma	1	8	15	22	29
We · Mi · Me	2	9	16	23	30
Th · Ju · Je	3	10	17	24	1
Fr · Vi · Ve	4	11	18	25	2
Sa · Sá · Sa	5	12	19	26	3
Su · Do · Di	6	13	20	27	4

30 Sunday | Domingo | Dimanche

Monday | Lunes | Lundi

31

Tuesday | Martes | Mardi

1

Wednesday | Miércoles | Mercredi

2

Dentist 4PM

481-1420

~~Ann Marie B day~~

Thursday | Jueves | Jeudi

3

Friday | Viernes | Vendredi

4

Saturday | Sábado | Samedi

5

Week	37	38	39	40	41
Mo·Lu·Lu	7	14	21	28	5
Tu·Ma·Ma	8	15	22	29	6
We·Mi·Me	9	16	23	30	7
Th·Ju·Je	10	17	24	1	8
Fr·Vi·Ve	11	18	25	2	9
Sa·Sá·Sa	12	19	26	3	10
Su·Do·Di	13	20	27	4	11

6

Sunday | Domingo | Dimanche

SIA WAR-DANCER

SAGUARO HARVEST – PIMA

Monday | Lunes | Lundi

7

(USA) Labor Day
(CDN) Labour Day | Fête du Travail

Tuesday | Martes | Mardi

8

Wednesday | Miércoles | Mercredi

9

Thursday | Jueves | Jeudi

10

Friday | Viernes | Vendredi

11

Donated Mission Pueblo 483-2001

Saturday | Sábado | Samedi

12

Christin Smith

Week	38	39	40	41	42
Mo·Lu·Lu	14	21	28	5	12
Tu·Ma·Ma	15	22	29	6	13
We·Mi·Me	16	23	30	7	14
Th·Ju·Je	17	24	1	8	15
Fr·Vi·Ve	18	25	2	9	16
Sa·Sá·Sa	19	26	3	10	17
Su·Do·Di	20	27	4	11	18

13 Sunday | Domingo | Dimanche

September | Septiembre | Septembre **1998**

Monday | Lunes | Lundi

14

Tuesday | Martes | Mardi

MISSION PUEBLO NOENO

✗

15

Wednesday | Miércoles | Mercredi

16

Thursday | Jueves | Jeudi

17

Friday | Viernes | Vendredi

18

Saturday | Sábado | Samedi

19

Week	39	40	41	42	43
Mo · Lu · Lu	21	28	5	12	19
Tu · Ma · Ma	22	29	6	13	20
We · Mi · Me	23	30	7	14	21
Th · Ju · Je	24	1	8	15	22
Fr · Vi · Ve	25	2	9	16	23
Sa · Sá · Sa	26	3	10	17	24
Su · Do · Di	27	4	11	18	25

20 Sunday | Domingo | Dimanche

WATCHING THE DANCERS

TWO MOONS – CHEYENNE

September | Septiembre | Septembre **1998**

Monday | Lunes | Lundi **21**

Tuesday | Martes | Mardi **22**

Wednesday | Miércoles | Mercredi **23**

Thursday | Jueves | Jeudi **24**

Friday | Viernes | Vendredi **25**

Saturday | Sábado | Sá

Week	40	41	4
Mo·Lu·Lu	28	5	1
Tu·Ma·Ma	29	6	1
We·Mi·Me	30	7	1.
Th·Ju·Je	1	8	1
Fr·Vi·Ve	2	9	1(
Sa·Sá·Sa	3	10	1;
Su·Do·Di	4	11	18

793-6141

H. REX GREENE, M.D.
~~STEPHEN C. KOEHLER, M.D.~~
C. PAUL SPEARS, M.D.
~~MONTY B.~~ POLONSKY, M.D.

HUNTINGTON CANCER CENTER
10 CONGRESS STREET
SUITE 340
PASADENA, CALIFORNIA 91105
(626) 568-9952 • FAX (626) 568-8096

397-3737

Monday | Lunes | Lundi

28

Tuesday | Martes | Mardi

29

Wednesday | Miércoles | Mercredi

30

Thursday | Jueves | Jeudi

1

Atlantic Tire
Romain + Fairfax

Friday | Viernes | Vendredi

2

Saturday | Sábado | Samedi

3

Week	41	42	43	44	45
Mo·Lu·Lu	5	12	19	26	2
Tu·Ma·Ma	6	13	20	27	3
We·Mi·Me	7	14	21	28	4
Th·Ju·Je	8	15	22	29	5
Fr·Vi·Ve	9	16	23	30	6
Sa·Sá·Sa	10	17	24	31	7
Su·Do·Di	11	18	25	1	8

4

Sunday | Domingo | Dimanche

TRAVELLING – ATSINA

ÁKATSIM-ATSISSI (WHISTLE SMOKE) – PIEGAN

Monday | Lunes | Lundi   **5**

Tuesday | Martes | Mardi   **6**

Wednesday | Miércoles | Mercredi   **7**

Thursday | Jueves | Jeudi   **8**

Friday | Viernes | Vendredi   **9**

Dr. Wang
310-888-1108

Saturday | Sábado | Samedi   **10**

Week	42	43	44	45	46
Mo·Lu·Lu	12	19	26	2	9
Tu·Ma·Ma	13	20	27	3	10
We·Mi·Me	14	21	28	4	11
Th·Ju·Je	15	22	29	5	12
Fr·Vi·Ve	16	23	30	6	13
Sa·Sá·Sa	17	24	31	7	14
Su·Do·Di	18	25	1	8	15

11   Sunday | Domingo | Dimanche

October | Octubre | Octobre **1998**

Monday | Lunes | Lundi

USA Columbus Day
CDN Thanksgiving Day | Action de Grâces

12

OFF

Tuesday | Martes | Mardi

13

Wednesday | Miércoles | Mercredi

14

Thursday | Jueves | Jeudi

15

SOUTHWEST: 800-435-9792

Friday | Viernes | Vendredi

16

Saturday | Sábado | Samedi

17

Week	43	44	45	46	47
Mo · Lu · Lu	19	26	2	9	16
Tu · Ma · Ma	20	27	3	10	17
We · Mi · Me	21	28	4	11	18
Th · Ju · Je	22	29	5	12	19
Fr · Vi · Ve	23	30	6	13	20
Sa · Sá · Sa	24	31	7	14	21
Su · Do · Di	25	1	8	15	22

18

Sunday | Domingo | Dimanche

WOMAN'S COSTUME AND BABY SWING – ASSINIBOIN

A CHIPEWYAN TIPI AMONG THE ASPENS

October | Octubre | Octobre **1998**

Monday | Lunes | Lundi

19

Tuesday | Martes | Mardi

20

2 PM DOCTOR

Wednesday | Miércoles | Mercredi

21

Thursday | Jueves | Jeudi

22

Friday | Viernes | Vendredi

23

3PM Doctor

Saturday | Sábado | Samedi

24

Week	44	45	46	47	48
Mo · Lu · Lu	26	2	9	16	23
Tu · Ma · Ma	27	3	10	17	24
We · Mi · Me	28	4	11	18	25
Th · Ju · Je	29	5	12	19	26
Fr · Vi · Ve	30	6	13	20	27
Sa · Sá · Sa	31	7	14	21	28
Su · Do · Di	1	8	15	22	29

25 Sunday | Domingo | Dimanche

Monday | Lunes | Lundi

26

Tuesday | Martes | Mardi

27

Wednesday | Miércoles | Mercredi

28

Thursday | Jueves | Jeudi

29

Friday | Viernes | Vendredi

30

Saturday | Sábado | Samedi

31

Week	45	46	47	48	49
Mo·Lu·Lu	2	9	16	23	30
Tu·Ma·Ma	3	10	17	24	1
We·Mi·Me	4	11	18	25	2
Th·Ju·Je	5	12	19	26	3
Fr·Vi·Ve	6	13	20	27	4
Sa·Sá·Sa	7	14	21	28	5
Su·Do·Di	8	15	22	29	6

1 Sunday | Domingo | Dimanche

FLATHEAD WARRIOR

DANCING TO RESTORE AN ECLIPSED MOON – QÁGYUHL

November | Noviembre | Novembre **1998**

Monday | Lunes | Lundi

2

Cont. United Am W: 800·235 9292₁₃₀
Reno - 800 - 736 - 6247 - $230⁰⁰ || UASISX   GAQKUG   #943 NOON -
Delta: 386 - 5510   8AM   Priceline: 774-2354   SoWest: 156⁰⁰ - 161⁰⁰   120 PM
   #943

Tuesday | Martes | Mardi

3

Wednesday | Miércoles | Mercredi

4

Thursday | Jueves | Jeudi

5

Friday | Viernes | Vendredi

6

Saturday | Sábado | Samedi

7

Week	46	47	48	49	50
Mo · Lu · Lu	9	16	23	30	7
Tu · Ma · Ma	10	17	24	1	8
We · Mi · Me	11	18	25	2	9
Th · Ju · Je	12	19	26	3	10
Fr · Vi · Ve	13	20	27	4	11
Sa · Sá · Sa	14	21	28	5	12
Su · Do · Di	15	22	29	6	13

8 Sunday | Domingo | Dimanche

November | Noviembre | Novembre **1998**

Monday | Lunes | Lundi **9**

Tuesday | Martes | Mardi **10**

Wednesday | Miércoles | Mercredi **11**

(USA) Veterans' Day
(CDN) Remembrance Day | Jour du Souvenir

Thursday | Jueves | Jeudi **12**

Friday | Viernes | Vendredi **13**

Saturday | Sábado | Samedi **14**

Dr. Smidt
310 828-1235

Week	47	48	49	50	51
Mo·Lu·Lu	16	23	30	7	14
Tu·Ma·Ma	17	24	1	8	15
We·Mi·Me	18	25	2	9	16
Th·Ju·Je	19	26	3	10	17
Fr·Vi·Ve	20	27	4	11	18
Sa·Sá·Sa	21	28	5	12	19
Su·Do·Di	22	29	6	13	20

Sunday | Domingo | Dimanche **15**

A PAINTED TIPI – ASSINIBOIN

OFFERING TO THE SUN – SAN ILDEFONSO

November | Noviembre | Novembre **1998**

Monday | Lunes | Lundi

16

Tuesday | Martes | Mardi

17

Wednesday | Miércoles | Mercredi

18

Thursday | Jueves | Jeudi

19

Friday | Viernes | Vendredi

20

Saturday | Sábado | Samedi

21

Week	48	49	50	51	52
Mo·Lu·Lu	23	30	7	14	21
Tu·Ma·Ma	24	1	8	15	22
We·Mi·Me	25	2	9	16	23
Th·Ju·Je	26	3	10	17	24
Fr·Vi·Ve	27	4	11	18	25
Sa·Sá·Sa	28	5	12	19	26
Su·Do·Di	29	6	13	20	27

22 Sunday | Domingo | Dimanche

November | Noviembre | Novembre **1998**

Monday | Lunes | Lundi

23

DOCTOR

Tuesday | Martes | Mardi

24

Wednesday | Miércoles | Mercredi **25**

DOCTOR HOSP.

Thursday | Jueves | Jeudi

26

(USA) Thanksgiving Day

Friday | Viernes | Vendredi

27

Saturday | Sábado | Samedi

28

Week	49	50	51	52	53
Mo·Lu·Lu	30	7	14	21	28
Tu·Ma·Ma	1	8	15	22	29
We·Mi·Me	2	9	16	23	30
Th·Ju·Je	3	10	17	24	31
Fr·Vi·Ve	4	11	18	25	1
Sa·Sá·Sa	5	12	19	26	2
Su·Do·Di	6	13	20	27	3

29 Sunday | Domingo | Dimanche

PEYOTE DRUMMER

IN THE MEDICINE-LODGE – ARIKARA

Monday | Lunes | Lundi

30

~~8:45 DR. GUILIANO~~

Tuesday | Martes | Mardi

1

213-977-1297
DR JAMES Corker

Wednesday | Miércoles | Mercredi

2

Thursday | Jueves | Jeudi

3

Friday | Viernes | Vendredi

4

Saturday | Sábado | Samedi

5

Week	50	51	52	53	1
Mo·Lu·Lu	7	14	21	28	4
Tu·Ma·Ma	8	15	22	29	5
We·Mi·Me	9	16	23	30	6
Th·Ju·Je	10	17	24	31	7
Fr·Vi·Ve	11	18	25	1	8
Sa·Sá·Sa	12	19	26	2	9
Su·Do·Di	13	20	27	3	10

6 Sunday | Domingo | Dimanche

December | Diciembre | Décembre **1998**

Monday | Lunes | Lundi **7**

9:30 CHECK
DR. ~~HUTCHISON~~ GIULIANO

Tuesday | Martes | Mardi **8**

Wednesday | Miércoles | Mercredi **9**

Thursday | Jueves | Jeudi **10**

HAIRWORKS-818-957-4247

Friday | Viernes | Vendredi **11**

Saturday | Sábado | Samedi **12**

Week	51	52	53	1	2
Mo·Lu·Lu	14	21	28	4	11
Tu·Ma·Ma	15	22	29	5	12
We·Mi·Me	16	23	30	6	13
Th·Ju·Je	17	24	31	7	14
Fr·Vi·Ve	18	25	1	8	15
Sa·Sá·Sa	19	26	2	9	16
Su·Do·Di	20	27	3	10	17

13 Sunday | Domingo | Dimanche

CROW EAGLE – PIEGAN

A HAMATSA COSTUME – NAKOAKTOK

Monday | Lunes | Lundi **14**

8-4 M-Th.

Dr. Melanson 705-735-1060
Rita Michaelia 735-1061 FAX
(Michael Kuselias)   HARCUT 6:30pm

Tuesday | Martes | Mardi **15**

Nav Health
241 Mineto Pt. Rd. Barrie. ONT
L4N4C4

Wednesday | Miércoles | Mercredi **16**

Novantheron
Adriamycin   705-466-2015 Marie
3:30 Dr. SAAUM   2774F Stevenson

$1850 per. day   630pm/1000

Thursday | Jueves | Jeudi **17**

310-453-5654

Friday | Viernes | Vendredi **18**

Saturday | Sábado | Samedi **19**

Week	52	53	1	2	3
Mo·Lu·Lu	21	28	4	11	18
Tu·Ma·Ma	22	29	5	12	19
We·Mi·Me	23	30	6	13	20
Th·Ju·Je	24	31	7	14	21
Fr·Vi·Ve	25	1	8	15	22
Sa·Sá·Sa	26	2	9	16	23
Su·Do·Di	27	3	10	17	24

20 Sunday | Domingo | Dimanche

December | Diciembre | Décembre **1998**

Monday | Lunes | Lundi

21

Tuesday | Martes | Mardi

22

Wednesday | Miércoles | Mercredi

23

OFF / 1/2 day

Thursday | Jueves | Jeudi

24

Friday | Viernes | Vendredi

Christmas Day | Noël

25

Saturday | Sábado | Samedi

26

Week	53	1	2	3	4
Mo·Lu·Lu	28	4	11	18	25
Tu·Ma·Ma	29	5	12	19	26
We·Mi·Me	30	6	13	20	27
Th·Ju·Je	31	7	14	21	28
Fr·Vi·Ve	1	8	15	22	29
Sa·Sá·Sa	2	9	16	23	30
Su·Do·Di	3	10	17	24	31

27 Sunday | Domingo | Dimanche

QUILCENE BOY

A FAMILY GROUP – NOATAK

Monday | Lunes | Lundi

28

Tuesday | Martes | Mardi

29

VACATION

Wednesday | Miércoles | Mercredi

30

Thursday | Jueves | Jeudi

31

Friday | Viernes | Vendredi

New Year's Day | Jour de l'An

1

Saturday | Sábado | Samedi

2

Week	1	2	3	4	5
Mo·Lu·Lu	4	11	18	25	1
Tu·Ma·Ma	5	12	19	26	2
We·Mi·Me	6	13	20	27	3
Th·Ju·Je	7	14	21	28	4
Fr·Vi·Ve	8	15	22	29	5
Sa·Sá·Sa	9	16	23	30	6
Su·Do·Di	10	17	24	31	7

3 Sunday | Domingo | Dimanche

January 5   7:30 AM   outpatient lab
Blood   Radiology

Public Holidays 1998 | Feiertage 1998 | Jours fériés pour 1998 | Días festivos en 1998

(A)
Österreich
1.1	Neujahr
6.1	Heilige Drei Könige
12.4	Ostersonntag
13.4	Ostermontag
1.5	Tag der Arbeit
21.5	Christi Himmelfahrt
31.5	Pfingstsonntag
1.6	Pfingstmontag
11.6	Fronleichnam
15.8	Mariä Himmelfahrt
26.10	Nationalfeiertag
1.11	Allerheiligen
8.12	Mariä Empfängnis
25.12	Christtag
26.12	Stefanitag

(AUS)
Australia
1.1	New Year's Day
26.1	Australia Day
10.4	Good Friday
12.4	Easter Sunday
13.4	Easter Monday
25.4	Anzac Day
25.12	Christmas Day
26.12	Boxing Day
28.12	Public Holiday

(B)
Belgique | België
1.1	Nouvel An	Nieuwjaar
12.4	Pâques	Pasen
13.4	Lundi de Pâques	Paasmaandag
1.5	Fête du Travail	Feest van de Arbeid
21.5	Ascension
	Onze-Lieve-Heer-Hemelvaart
31.5	Pentecôte	Pinksteren
1.6	Lundi de Pentecôte
	Pinkstermaandag
21.7	Fête Nationale
	Nationale Feestdag
15.8	Assomption	Onze-Lieve-
	Vrouw-Hemelvaart
1.11	Toussaint	Allerheiligen
2.11	Jour des Morts	Allerzielen
11.11	Armistice	Wapenstilstand
25.12	Noël	Kerstmis
26.12	Lendemain de Noël
	Tweede Kerstdag

(BR)
Brasil
1.1	Ano Novo
24.2	Carnaval
10.4	Sexta-feira da Paixão
12.4	Páscoa
21.4	Tiradentes
1.5	Dia do Trabalho
11.6	Corpus Christi
7.9	Independência do Brasil (1822)
12.10	Nossa Senhora Aparecida
2.11	Finados
15.11	Proclamação da República (1889)
25.12	Natal

(C)
Catalunya
1.1	Any Nou
6.1	Epifania
9.4	Dijous Sant
10.4	Divendres Sant
12.4	Pasqua
13.4	Dilluns de Pasqua
1.5	Festa del Treball
24.6	Sant Joan
15.8	L'Assumpció
12.10	Festa de la Hispanitat
1.11	Tots Sants
6.12	Dia de la Constitució
8.12	La Immaculada
25.12	Nadal
26.12	Sant Esteve

(CDN)
Canada
1.1	New Year's Day	Jour de l'An
10.4	Good Friday	Vendredi Saint
12.4	Easter Sunday	Pâques
18.5	Victoria Day
	Fête de la Reine et de Dollard
24.6	Québec's National Holiday
	Fête Nationale du Québec
1.7	Canada Day	Jour de la Confédération
7.9	Labour Day	Fête du Travail
12.10	Thanksgiving Day	Action de Grâces
11.11	Remembrance Day	Jour du Souvenir
25.12	Christmas Day	Noël

(CH)
Schweiz | Suisse | Svizzera
1.1	Neujahr	Nouvel An	Capo d'Anno
1.3	Tag der Kranken	Journée
	des malades	Giornata dei malati
10.4	Karfreitag	Vendredi Saint
	Venerdì Santo
12.4	Ostern	Pâques	Pasqua
13.4	Ostermontag	Lundi de
	Pâques	Lunedì dell'Angelo
10.5	Muttertag	Journée des mères
	Giornata della madre
21.5	Auffahrt	Ascension	Ascensione
31.5	Pfingsten	Pentecôte	Pentecoste
1.6	Pfingstmontag	Lundi de Pentecôte
	Lunedì di Pentecoste
1.8	Bundesfeiertag	Fête nationale suisse
	Festa nazionale svizzera
20.9	Eidg. Bettag	Jeûne
	fédéral	Digiuno federale
25.12	Weihnachten	Noël	Natale
26.12	Stefanstag	S. Etienne	S. Stefano

(D)
**Bundesrepublik
Deutschland**
1.1	Neujahr
6.1	Heilige Drei Könige (teilweise)
10.4	Karfreitag
12.4	Ostersonntag
13.4	Ostermontag
1.5	Maifeiertag
21.5	Christi Himmelfahrt
31.5	Pfingstsonntag
1.6	Pfingstmontag
11.6	Fronleichnam (teilweise)
15.8	Mariä Himmelfahrt (teilweise)
3.10	Tag der Deutschen Einheit
31.10	Reformationstag (teilweise)
1.11	Allerheiligen (teilweise)
18.11	Buß- und Bettag (teilweise)
25.12	1. Weihnachtstag
26.12	2. Weihnachtstag

(DK)
Danmark
1.1	Nytår
9.4	Skærtorsdag
10.4	Langfredag
12.4	Påske
13.4	Påske
8.5	St. Bededag
21.5	Kristi himmelfartsdag
31.5	Pinse
1.6	Pinse
5.6	Grundlovsdag
25.12	Jul
26.12	Jul

(E)
España
1.1	Año Nuevo
6.1	Epifanía
10.4	Viernes Santo
12.4	Pascua
1.5	Fiesta del Trabajo
15.8	Asunción
12.10	Fiesta Nacional
1.11	Todos los Santos
6.12	Día de la Constitución
8.12	Inmaculada Concepción
25.12	Natividad del Señor

(F)
France
1.1	Jour de l'An
12.4	Pâques
13.4	Lundi de Pâques
1.5	Fête du Travail
21.5	Ascension	Fête de la Libération
31.5	Pentecôte
1.6	Lundi de Pentecôte
14.7	Fête Nationale
15.8	Assomption
1.11	Toussaint
11.11	Armistice 1918
25.12	Noël

(FIN)
Suomi
1.1	Uudenvuodenpäivä
6.1	Loppiainen
10.4	Pitkäperjantai
12.4	Pääsiäispäivä
13.4	2. Pääsiäispäivä
1.5	Vapunpäivä
21.5	Helatorstai
31.5	Helluntaipäivä
20.6	Juhannuspäivä

1.11	Pyhäinpäivä
6.12	Itsenäisyyspäivä
25.12	Joulupäivä
26.12	Tapaninpäivä

Ⓘ
Italia
1.1	Capodanno
6.1	Epifania
12.4	Pasqua
13.4	Lunedì di Pasqua
25.4	Anniversario della Liberazione
1.5	Festa del Lavoro
15.8	Ascensione di Maria Vergine
1.11	Tutti i Santi
8.12	Immacolata Concezione
25.12	Natale
26.12	Santo Stefano

Ⓘ̲ⓡ̲ⓛ̲
Ireland
1.1	New Year's Day
17.3	Saint Patrick's Day
12.4	Easter Sunday
13.4	Easter Monday
4.5	First Monday in May
1.6	First Monday in June
3.8	First Monday in August
26.10	Last Monday in October
25.12	Christmas Day
26.12	Saint Stephen's Day
28.12	Public Holiday

Ⓙ
Japan
1.1	New Year's Day
15.1	Coming-of-Age Day
11.2	Commemoration of the Founding of the Nation
21.3	Vernal Equinox Day
29.4	Greenery Day
3.5	Constitution Day
5.5	Children's Day
20.7	Marine Day
15.9	Respect-for-the-Aged Day
23.9	Autumn Equinox Day
10.10	Health-Sports Day
3.11	Culture Day
23.11	Labor-Thanksgiving Day
23.12	Emperor's Birthday

Ⓝ
Norge
1.1	Nyttårsdag
5.4	Palmesøndag
9.4	Skjærtorsdag
10.4	Langfredag
12.4	1. påskedag
13.4	2. påskedag
1.5	Offentlig høytidsdag
17.5	Grunnlovsdag
21.5	Kristi himmelfartsdag
31.5	1. pinsedag
1.6	2. pinsedag
25.12	1. juledag
26.12	2. juledag

Ⓝ̲ⓛ̲
Nederland
1.1	Nieuwjaarsdag
10.4	Goede Vrijdag
12.4	1e Paasdag
13.4	2e Paasdag
30.4	Koninginnedag
21.5	Hemelvaartsdag
31.5	1e Pinksterdag
1.6	2e Pinksterdag
25.12	1e Kerstdag
26.12	2e Kerstdag

Ⓝ̲ⓩ̲
New Zealand
1.1	New Year's Day
6.2	Waitangi Day
10.4	Good Friday
12.4	Easter Sunday
13.4	Easter Monday
25.4	Anzac Day
1.6	Queen's Birthday
26.10	Labour Day
25.12	Christmas Day
26.12	Boxing Day
28.12	Public Holiday

Ⓟ
Portugal
1.1	Ano Novo
10.4	Sexta-feira Santa
12.4	Páscoa
25.4	Dia da Liberdade
1.5	Festa do Trabalho
10.6	Dia Nacional
11.6	Corpo de Deus
15.8	Assunção de Nossa Senhora
5.10	Implantação da República
1.11	Todos os Santos
1.12	Dia da Restauração
8.12	Imaculada Conceição
25.12	Natal

Ⓢ
Sverige
1.1	Nyårsdagen
6.1	Trettondedag Jul
10.4	Långfredagen
12.4	Påskdagen
13.4	Annandag Påsk
1.5	Första Maj
21.5	Kristi Himmelsfärds dag
31.5	Pingstdagen
1.6	Annandag Pingst
20.6	Midsommardagen
31.10	Alla Helgons dag
25.12	Juldagen
26.12	Annandag Jul

Ⓤ̲ⓚ̲
United Kingdom
1.1	New Year's Day
2.1	Bank Holiday (Scotland only)
17.3	Saint Patrick's Day (Northern Ireland)
10.4	Good Friday
12.4	Easter Sunday
13.4	Easter Monday (except Scotland)
4.5	May Bank Holiday
25.5	Spring Bank Holiday
3.8	Summer Bank Holiday (Scotland only)
31.8	Summer Bank Holiday (except Scotland)
25.12	Christmas Day
26.12	Boxing Day
28.12	Public Holiday

Ⓤ̲ⓢ̲ⓐ̲
United States
1.1	New Year's Day
19.1	Martin Luther King Day
16.2	Presidents' Day
12.4	Easter Sunday
25.5	Memorial Day
4.7	Independence Day
7.9	Labor Day
12.10	Columbus Day
11.11	Veterans' Day
26.11	Thanksgiving Day
25.12	Christmas Day

Ⓩ̲ⓐ̲
South Africa
1.1	New Year's Day
21.3	Human Rights Day
31.3	Family Day
10.4	Good Friday
12.4	Easter Sunday
27.4	Constitution Day
1.5	Worker's Day
16.6	Youth Day
9.8	National Women's Day
24.9	Heritage Day
16.12	Day of Reconciliation
25.12	Christmas Day
26.12	Day of Goodwill

Some international holidays may be subject to change.

Year Planner | Plan Anual | Planning **1999**

January | Enero | Janvier		February | Febrero | Février		March | Marzo | Mars		April | Abril | Avril	
1 Fr		1 Mo	**5**	1 Mo	**9**	1 Th	
2 Sa		2 Tu		2 Tu		2 Fr	
3 Su		3 We		3 We		3 Sa	
4 Mo	**1**	4 Th		4 Th		4 Su	
5 Tu		5 Fr		5 Fr		5 Mo	**14**
6 We		6 Sa		6 Sa		6 Tu	
7 Th		7 Su		7 Su		7 We	
8 Fr		8 Mo	**6**	8 Mo	**10**	8 Th	
9 Sa		9 Tu		9 Tu		9 Fr	
10 Su		10 We		10 We		10 Sa	
11 Mo	**2**	11 Th		11 Th		11 Su	
12 Tu		12 Fr		12 Fr		12 Mo	**15**
13 We		13 Sa		13 Sa		13 Tu	
14 Th		14 Su		14 Su		14 We	
15 Fr		15 Mo	**7**	15 Mo	**11**	15 Th	
16 Sa		16 Tu		16 Tu		16 Fr	
17 Su		17 We		17 We		17 Sa	
18 Mo	**3**	18 Th		18 Th		18 Su	
19 Tu		19 Fr		19 Fr		19 Mo	**16**
20 We		20 Sa		20 Sa		20 Tu	
21 Th		21 Su		21 Su		21 We	
22 Fr		22 Mo	**8**	22 Mo	**12**	22 Th	
23 Sa		23 Tu		23 Tu		23 Fr	
24 Su		24 We		24 We		24 Sa	
25 Mo	**4**	25 Th		25 Th		25 Su	
26 Tu		26 Fr		26 Fr		26 Mo	**17**
27 We		27 Sa		27 Sa		27 Tu	
28 Th		28 Su		28 Su		28 We	
29 Fr				29 Mo	**13**	29 Th	
30 Sa				30 Tu		30 Fr	
31 Su				31 We			

Year Planner | Plan Anual | Planning **1999**

May | Mayo | Mai		June | Junio | Juin		July | Julio | Juillet		August | Agosto | Août	
1 Sa		1 Tu		1 Th		1 Su	
2 Su		2 We		2 Fr		2 Mo	**31**
3 Mo	**18**	3 Th		3 Sa		3 Tu	
4 Tu		4 Fr		4 Su		4 We	
5 We		5 Sa		5 Mo	**27**	5 Th	
6 Th		6 Su		6 Tu		6 Fr	
7 Fr		7 Mo	**23**	7 We		7 Sa	
8 Sa		8 Tu		8 Th		8 Su	
9 Su		9 We		9 Fr		9 Mo	**32**
10 Mo	**19**	10 Th		10 Sa		10 Tu	
11 Tu		11 Fr		11 Su		11 We	
12 We		12 Sa		12 Mo	**28**	12 Th	
13 Th		13 Su		13 Tu		13 Fr	
14 Fr		14 Mo	**24**	14 We		14 Sa	
15 Sa		15 Tu		15 Th		15 Su	
16 Su		16 We		16 Fr		16 Mo	**33**
17 Mo	**20**	17 Th		17 Sa		17 Tu	
18 Tu		18 Fr		18 Su		18 We	
19 We		19 Sa		19 Mo	**29**	19 Th	
20 Th		20 Su		20 Tu		20 Fr	
21 Fr		21 Mo	**25**	21 We		21 Sa	
22 Sa		22 Tu		22 Th		22 Su	
23 Su		23 We		23 Fr		23 Mo	**34**
24 Mo	**21**	24 Th		24 Sa		24 Tu	
25 Tu		25 Fr		25 Su		25 We	
26 We		26 Sa		26 Mo	**30**	26 Th	
27 Th		27 Su		27 Tu		27 Fr	
28 Fr		28 Mo	**26**	28 We		28 Sa	
29 Sa		29 Tu		29 Th		29 Su	
30 Su		30 We		30 Fr		30 Mo	**35**
31 Mo	**22**			31 Sa		31 Tu	

Year Planner | Plan Anual | Planning **1999**

September | Septiembre | Septemb		October | Octubre | Octobre		November | Noviembre | Novemb		December | Diciembre | Décemb	
1 We		1 Fr		1 Mo	**44**	1 We	
2 Th		2 Sa		2 Tu		2 Th	
3 Fr		3 Su		3 We		3 Fr	
4 Sa		4 Mo	**40**	4 Th		4 Sa	
5 Su		5 Tu		5 Fr		5 Su	
6 Mo	**36**	6 We		6 Sa		6 Mo	**49**
7 Tu		7 Th		7 Su		7 Tu	
8 We		8 Fr		8 Mo	**45**	8 We	
9 Th		9 Sa		9 Tu		9 Th	
10 Fr		10 Su		10 We		10 Fr	
11 Sa		11 Mo	**41**	11 Th		11 Sa	
12 Su		12 Tu		12 Fr		12 Su	
13 Mo	**37**	13 We		13 Sa		13 Mo	**50**
14 Tu		14 Th		14 Su		14 Tu	
15 We		15 Fr		15 Mo	**46**	15 We	
16 Th		16 Sa		16 Tu		16 Th	
17 Fr		17 Su		17 We		17 Fr	
18 Sa		18 Mo	**42**	18 Th		18 Sa	
19 Su		19 Tu		19 Fr		19 Su	
20 Mo	**38**	20 We		20 Sa		20 Mo	**51**
21 Tu		21 Th		21 Su		21 Tu	
22 We		22 Fr		22 Mo	**47**	22 We	
23 Th		23 Sa		23 Tu		23 Th	
24 Fr		24 Su		24 We		24 Fr	
25 Sa		25 Mo	**43**	25 Th		25 Sa	
26 Su		26 Tu		26 Fr		26 Su	
27 Mo	**39**	27 We		27 Sa		27 Mo	**52**
28 Tu		28 Th		28 Su		28 Tu	
29 We		29 Fr		29 Mo	**48**	29 We	
30 Th		30 Sa		30 Tu		30 Th	
		31 Su				31 Fr	